100 All-Time

JAZZ GREATS

for Saxophone · Clarinet · Flute · Trumpet...

Exclusive Distributors: **Music Sales Limited** 8/9 Frith Street, London WIV 5TZ, England.
Music Sales Pty Limited 120 Rothschild Avenue Rosebery, NSW 2018, Australia.

Order No. AM950818 · ISBN 0-7119-3173-9 · This book © Copyright 1993, 1997 by Wise Publications
Visit the Internet Music Shop at http://www.musicsales.co.uk

Compiled by Peter Evans and Peter Lavender · Music arranged by Peter Lavender · Music processed by Upton and Skinner
Cover design by Chloë Alexander

Printed in the United Kingdom by The Bath Press, Bath

Your Guarantee of Quality

As publishers, we strive to produce every book to the highest commercial standards. The book has been carefully designed to minimise awkward page turns and to make playing from it a real pleasure. Particular care has been given to specifying acid-free, neutral-sized paper made from pulps which have not been elemental chlorine bleached. This pulp is from farmed sustainable forests and was produced with special regard for the environment. Throughout, the printing and binding have been planned to ensure a sturdy, attractive publication which should give years of enjoyment. If your copy fails to meet our high standards, please inform us and we will gladly replace it.

Music Sales' complete catalogue describes thousands of titles and is available in full colour sections by subject, direct from Music Sales Limited. Please state your areas of interest and send a cheque/postal order for £1.50 for postage to:
Music Sales Limited, Newmarket Road, Bury St. Edmunds, Suffolk IP33 3YB.

Wise Publications
London/New York/Sydney/Paris/Copenhagen/Madrid

B♭

I Wish I Knew How It Would Feel To Be Free

Words by Billy Taylor & Dick Dallas
Music by Billy Taylor

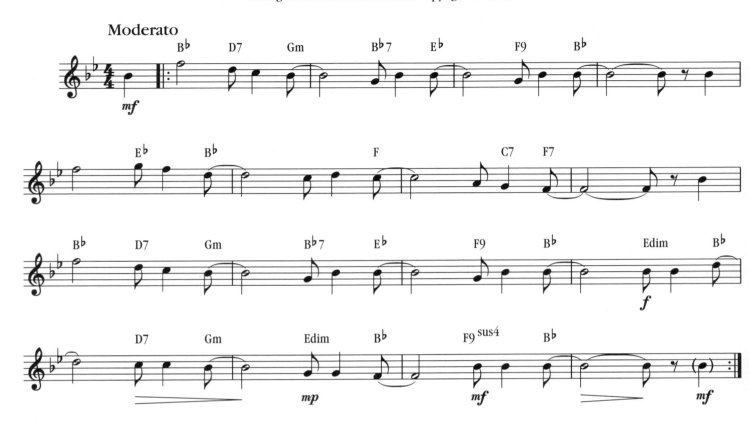

Intermission Riff

Words by Steve Graham
Music by Ray Wetzel

I Wish I Knew How It Would Feel To Be Free

Words by Billy Taylor & Dick Dallas
Music by Billy Taylor

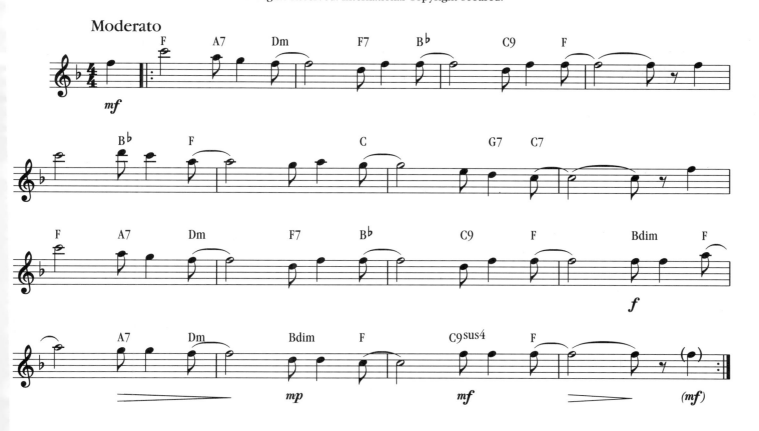

Intermission Riff

Words by Steve Graham
Music by Ray Wetzel

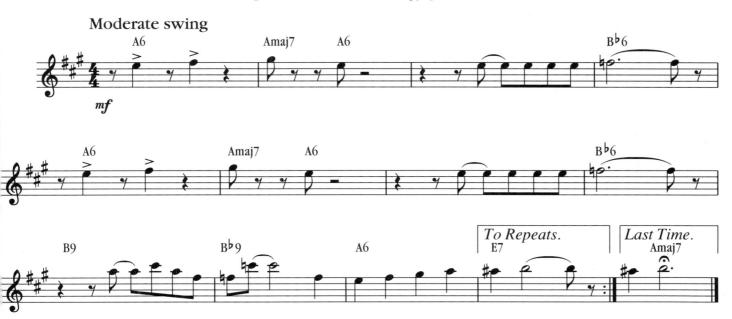

B♭

Soul Junction

By Red Garland

Slow groove

Hip Twist

By Stanley Turrentine

Moderate Blues

Soul Junction

By Red Garland

Slow groove

Hip Twist

By Stanley Turrentine

Moderate Blues

African Waltz
Words & Music By Galt MacDermot

African Waltz
Words & Music By Galt MacDermot

E♭

Bill Bailey, Won't You Please Come Home

Traditional

B♭

E♭ Bill Bailey, Won't You Please Come Home

Traditional

Black Coffee

Words & Music by Paul Francis Webster & Sonny Burke

Black Coffee
Words & Music by Paul Francis Webster & Sonny Burke

B♭

Chelsea Bridge
By Billy Strayhorn

E♭

Chelsea Bridge

By Billy Strayhorn

Canal Street Blues

By Joe "King" Oliver

B♭

Canal Street Blues

By Joe "King" Oliver

Cute

Words by Stanley Styne
Music by Neal Hefti

Cute

Words by Stanley Styne
Music by Neal Hefti

E♭

Bb Don't Dream Of Anybody But Me (Li'l Darlin')

Words by Bart Howard
Music by Neal Hefti

Don't Dream Of Anybody But Me (Li'l Darlin')

E♭

Words by Bart Howard
Music by Neal Hefti

B♭

Everything But You

By Duke Ellington, Harry James & Don George

E♭

Everything But You

By Duke Ellington, Harry James & Don George

In A Sentimental Mood

Words & Music by Duke Ellington, Irving Mills & Manny Kurtz

In A Sentimental Mood

Words & Music by Duke Ellington, Irving Mills & Manny Kurtz

Lean Baby

Words by Roy Alfred
Music by Bill May

Lean Baby

Words by Roy Alfred
Music by Bill May

E♭

Bark For Barksdale

By Gerry Mulligan

B♭

Bark For Barksdale

By Gerry Mulligan

E♭

B♭

Bernie's Tune

By Bernie Miller

Bernie's Tune

By Bernie Miller

E♭

How Insensitive

Music by Antonio Carlos Jobim
Original Lyrics by Vinicius De Moraes. English Lyrics by Norman Gimbel

B♭

E♭

How Insensitive

Music by Antonio Carlos Jobim
Original Lyrics by Vinicius De Moraes. English Lyrics by Norman Gimbel

B♭

Jersey Bounce

Music by Bobby Plater, Tiny Bradshaw & Edward Johnson
Words by Robert B. Wright

Jersey Bounce

Music by Bobby Plater, Tiny Bradshaw & Edward Johnson
Words by Robert B. Wright

E♭

B♭

Lemon Drop

By George Wallington

Lemon Drop

By George Wallington

Lush Life

Words & Music by Billy Strayhorn

Lush Life

Words & Music by Billy Strayhorn

B♭

Manhattan Spiritual
By Billy Maxted

Manhattan Spiritual

By Billy Maxted

E♭

Nine Twenty Special

Words by Bill Engvick
Music by Earl Warren

Nine Twenty Special

Words by Bill Engvick
Music by Earl Warren

E♭

Caravan

By Duke Ellington, Irving Mills & Juan Tizol

Caravan

By Duke Ellington, Irving Mills & Juan Tizol

Pompton Turnpike

Words & Music by Will Osborne & Dick Rogers

E♭

Pompton Turnpike
Words & Music by Will Osborne & Dick Rogers

Quiet Night Of Quiet Stars

English Words by Gene Lees
Music & Original Words by Antonio Carlos Jobim

B♭

E♭

Quiet Night Of Quiet Stars

English Words by Gene Lees
Music & Original Words by Antonio Carlos Jobim

Moderate Bossa Nova

B♭

Recado Bossa Nova (The Gift)

Words & Music by Djalma Ferreira & Luiz Antonio

E♭

Recado Bossa Nova (The Gift)

Words & Music by Djalma Ferreira & Luiz Antonio

B♭

Seven Eleven
By Carpenter & Williams

E♭

Seven Eleven
By Carpenter & Williams

Fast Bop

Someday (You'll Be Sorry)

Words & Music by Louis Armstrong

Someday (You'll Be Sorry)

Words & Music by Louis Armstrong

Stomp, Look And Listen

By Duke Ellington

Stomp, Look And Listen

By Duke Ellington

Take Five

By Paul Desmond

E♭

Take Five
By Paul Desmond

Walkin' Shoes

By Gerry Mulligan

Bb

Walkin' Shoes

By Gerry Mulligan

E♭

Bᵇ

Waltz For Debby
Music by Bill Evans
Words by Gene Lees

E♭

Waltz For Debby
Music by Bill Evans
Words by Gene Lees

B♭

Yesterdays
Music by Jerome Kern
Words by Otto Harbach

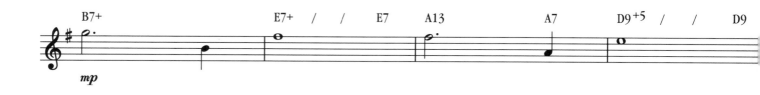

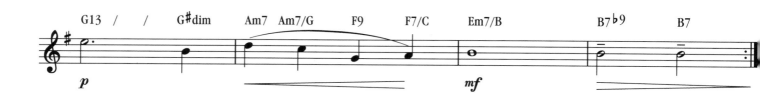

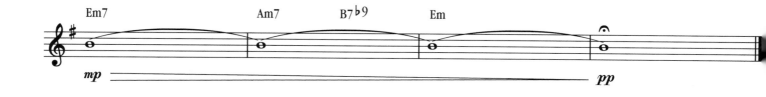

E♭

Yesterdays
Music by Jerome Kern
Words by Otto Harbach

Slow
8va opt.

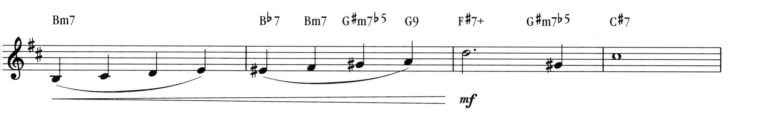

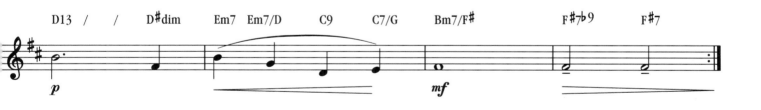

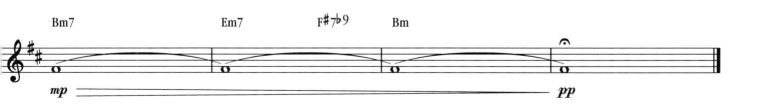

B♭

Yes Indeed (A Jive Spiritual)

Words & Music by Sy Oliver

Moderato

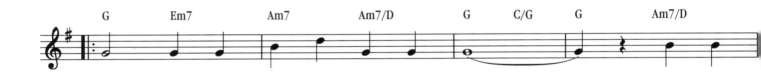

E♭

Yes Indeed (A Jive Spiritual)

Words & Music by Sy Oliver

Moderato

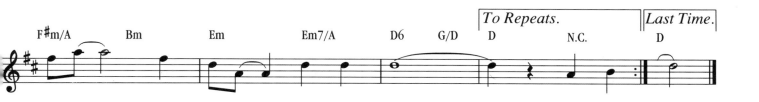

Yardbird Suite

By Charlie Parker

Yardbird Suite
By Charlie Parker

E♭

Ornithology

By Charlie Parker & Benny Harris

B♭

Ornithology

By Charlie Parker & Benny Harris

Satin Doll

Words by Johnny Mercer
Music by Duke Ellington & Billy Strayhorn

B♭

E♭

Satin Doll
Words by Johnny Mercer
Music by Duke Ellington & Billy Strayhorn

B♭

Solitude
Words by Eddie de Lange & Irving Mills
Music by Duke Ellington

Solitude
Words by Eddie de Lange & Irving Mills
Music by Duke Ellington

Tuxedo Junction

Words by Buddy Feyne
Music by Erskine Hawkins, William Johnson & Julian Dash

B♭

Tuxedo Junction

Words by Buddy Feyne
Music by Erskine Hawkins, William Johnson & Julian Dash

Mood Indigo

Words & Music by Duke Ellington, Irving Mills & Albany Bigard

E♭

Mood Indigo

Words & Music by Duke Ellington, Irving Mills & Albany Bigard

Angel Eyes

Words by Earl Brent
Music by Earl Dennis

Angel Eyes

Words by Earl Brent
Music by Earl Dennis

E♭

Moonglow

Words & Music by Will Hudson, Eddie de Lange & Irving Mills

Moonglow

Words & Music by Will Hudson, Eddie de Lange & Irving Mills

Fly Me To The Moon (In Other Words)

Words & Music by Bart Howard

Fly Me To The Moon (In Other Words)

Eb

Words & Music by Bart Howard

B♭

Midnight Sun

Words by Johnny Mercer
Music by Sonny Burke and Lionel Hampton

E♭

Midnight Sun

Words by Johnny Mercer
Music by Sonny Burke and Lionel Hampton

B♭

Lullaby Of Birdland

Music by George Shearing
Words by George David Weiss

Moderato

Lullaby Of Birdland

Music by George Shearing
Words by George David Weiss

E♭

B♭

Time's A-Wastin'

Words & Music by Duke Ellington, Mercer Ellington & Don George

Eb

Time's A-Wastin'

Words & Music by Duke Ellington, Mercer Ellington & Don George

Mississippi Mud

Words & Music by Harry Barris

B♭

Moderato

Mississippi Mud

Words & Music by Harry Barris

It's A Raggy Waltz

Music by Dave Brubeck

B♭

It's A Raggy Waltz
Music by Dave Brubeck

E♭

Lover Man (Oh Where Can You Be)

Bb

Words & Music by Jimmy Davies, Roger Ram Ramirez & Jimmy Sherman

Lover Man (Oh Where Can You Be)

Words & Music by Jimmy Davies, Roger Ram Ramirez & Jimmy Sherman

E♭

The Girl From Ipanema (Garota De Ipanema)

B♭

Original Words by Vinicius De Moraes
English Lyric by Norman Gimbel
Music by Antonio Carlos Jobim

The Girl From Ipanema (Garota De Ipanema)

E♭

Original Words by Vinicius De Moraes
English Lyric by Norman Gimbel
Music by Antonio Carlos Jobim

Take The 'A' Train

Words & Music by Billy Strayhorn

B♭

Take The 'A' Train

E♭

Words & Music by Billy Strayhorn

I'm Beginning To See The Light

Words & Music by Harry James, Duke Ellington, Johnny Hodges & Don George

I'm Beginning To See The Light

Words & Music by Harry James, Duke Ellington, Johnny Hodges & Don George

B♭

A Night In Tunisia

Music by Frank Paparelli & John "Dizzy" Gillespie
Words by Raymond Leveen

A Night In Tunisia

Music by Frank Paparelli & John "Dizzy" Gillespie
Words by Raymond Leveen

E♭

Desafinado
Music by Antonio Jobim

B♭

Desafinado
Music by Antonio Jobim

B♭

Early Autumn
Words by Johnny Mercer
Music by Ralph Burns & Woody Herman

Early Autumn

Words by Johnny Mercer
Music by Ralph Burns & Woody Herman

113

Perdido

Music by Juan Tizol
Words by Harry Lenk and Ervin Drake

B♭

Perdido
Music by Juan Tizol
Words by Harry Lenk and Ervin Drake

E♭

Basin Street Blues

Words & Music by Spencer Williams

B♭

E♭

Basin Street Blues
Words & Music by Spencer Williams

B♭

The Lonesome Road
Words by Gene Austin
Music by Nathaniel Shilkret

With Spirit

The Lonesome Road

Words by Gene Austin
Music by Nathaniel Shilkret

Is You Is, Or Is You Ain't (Ma' Baby)

Words and Music by Billy Austin & Louis Jordan

Is You Is, Or Is You Ain't (Ma' Baby)

Words and Music by Billy Austin & Louis Jordan

B♭

Django

by John Lewis

Slow

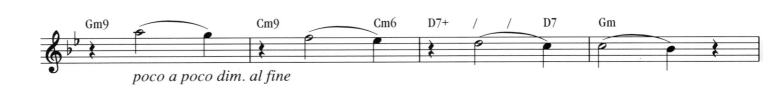

poco a poco dim. al fine

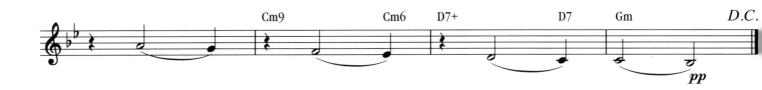

E♭

Django
by John Lewis

Slow

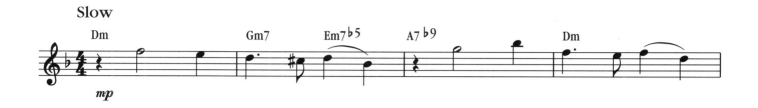

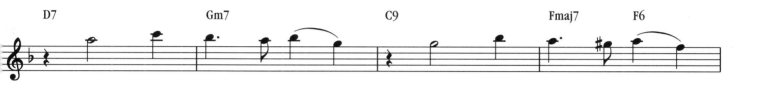

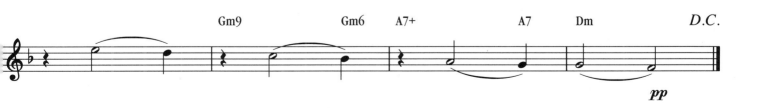

B♭

Drop Me Off In Harlem

Words by Nick Kenny
Music by Duke Ellington

Drop Me Off In Harlem

Words by Nick Kenny
Music by Duke Ellington

Flying Home

By Benny Goodman & Lionel Hampton

B♭

Flying Home

By Benny Goodman & Lionel Hampton

B♭

Good Bait
By Tadd Dameron & Count Basie

Good Bait

By Tadd Dameron & Count Basie

The Hawk Talks

By Louis Bellson

The Hawk Talks

By Louis Bellson

B♭

Manteca
Words & Music by Dizzy Gillespie & Gil Fuller

Manteca
Words & Music by Dizzy Gillespie & Gil Fuller

E♭

Moanin'

Words by Jon Hendricks
Music by Bobby Timmons

Moanin'

Words by Jon Hendricks
Music by Bobby Timmons

B♭

Night Train

Words by Oscar Washington and Lewis C. Simpkins
Music by Jimmy Forrest

Moderato

Night Train

Words by Oscar Washington and Lewis C. Simpkins
Music by Jimmy Forrest

B♭

Pent Up House

By Sonny Rollins

Moderato

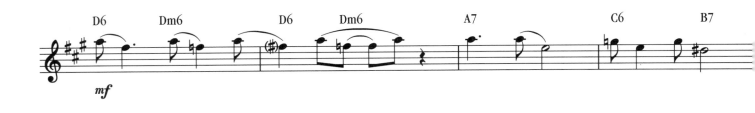

E♭

Pent Up House

By Sonny Rollins

Moderato

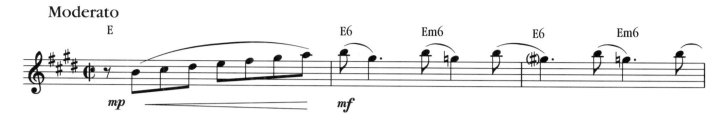

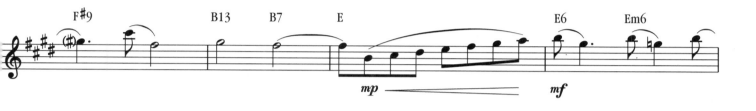

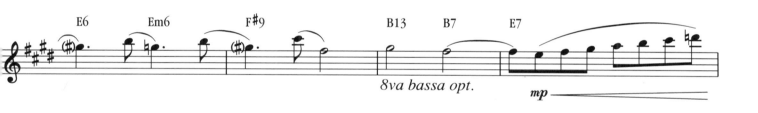

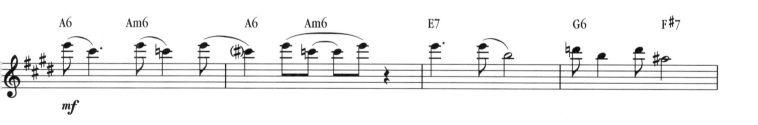

No Line
By Miles Davis

Moderato

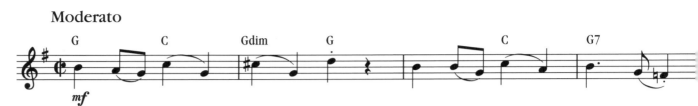

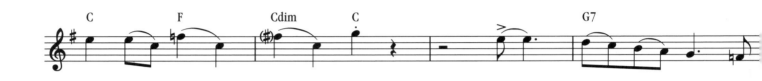

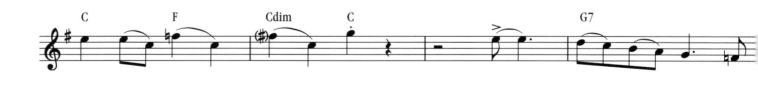

E♭

No Line
By Miles Davis

Moderato

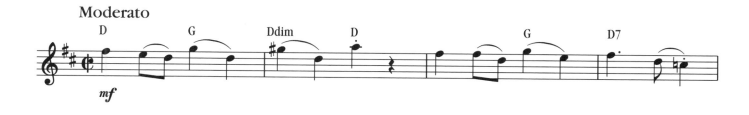

The Preacher

By Horace Silver

The Preacher

By Horace Silver

B♭

Meditation
Original Words By Newton Mendoca
English Lyric by Norman Gimbel
Music by Antonio Carlos Jobim

Moderate Bossa Nova

144

B♭

E♭

Meditation

Original Words by Newton Mendoca
English Lyric by Norman Gimbel
Music by Antonio Carlos Jobim

Moderate Bossa Nova

So Nice

Music & Original Lyrics by Marcoa Valle & Paulo Sergio Valle
English Lyrics by Norman Gimbel

B♭

Moderate Bossa Nova

So Nice

Music & Original Lyrics by Marcoa Valle & Paulo Sergio Valle
English Lyrics by Norman Gimbel

E♭

B♭

Red Top

Words & Music by Lionel Hampton & Ken Kynard

Moderate Bounce

Red Top

Words & Music by Lionel Hampton & Ken Kynard

Ruby, My Dear

By Thelonious Monk

B♭

Ruby, My Dear

By Thelonious Monk

Seven Come Eleven

By Benny Goodman & Charlie Christian

Seven Come Eleven

By Benny Goodman & Charlie Christian

B♭

Salt Peanuts
Words & Music by John "Dizzy" Gillespie & Kenny Clarke

Moderato

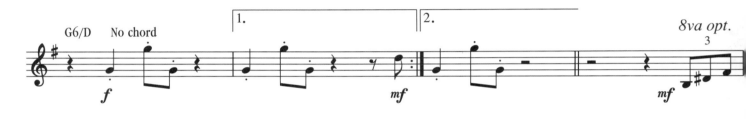

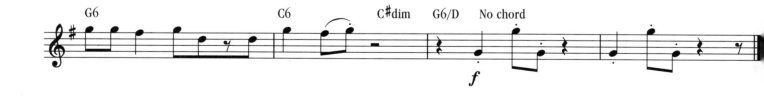

Eb

Salt Peanuts
Words & Music by John "Dizzy" Gillespie & Kenny Clarke

Moderato

Short Stop

By Shorty Rogers

Short Stop

By Shorty Rogers

Eb

Skin Deep

By Louis Bellson

Skin Deep

By Louis Bellson

Song Of The Jet

Original Words & Music by Antonio Carlos Jobim
English Words by Gene Lees

B♭

Moderate Bossa Nova

Song Of The Jet

Original Words & Music by Antonio Carlos Jobim
English Words by Gene Lees

E♭

Struttin' With Some Barbecue

Words by Don Raye
Music by Louis Armstrong

B♭

Struttin' With Some Barbecue

Words by Don Raye
Music by Louis Armstrong

E♭

B♭

Sweetheart Of Sigmund Freud

By Shorty Rogers

Sweetheart Of Sigmund Freud

By Shorty Rogers

Paul's Pal

By Sonny Rollins

Paul's Pal

By Sonny Rollins

E♭

Undecided
Words by Sid Robbin
Music by Charles Shavers

Undecided

Words by Sid Robbin
Music by Charles Shavers

B♭

Very Early

Music by Bill Evans
Words by Carol Hall

Moderate Jazz Waltz

Very Early

Music by Bill Evans
Words by Carol Hall

Way Down Yonder In New Orleans

B♭

Words & Music by Henry Creamer & Turner Layton

Way Down Yonder In New Orleans

E♭

Words & Music by Henry Creamer & Turner Layton

B♭

Tel Aviv
By Herbie Mann

Plaintively

E ♭

Tel Aviv
By Herbie Mann

Plaintively

Wheatland (from the "Canadian Suite")

Bb

By Oscar Peterson

Wheatland (from the "Canadian Suite")

E♭

By Oscar Peterson

Will You Still Be Mine

Words by Tom Adair
Music by Matt Dennis

Will You Still Be Mine

Words by Tom Adair
Music by Matt Dennis

Weep No More

By Dave Brubeck

Weep No More

By Dave Brubeck

B♭

Honeysuckle Rose

Music by Thomas "Fats" Waller
Words by Andy Razaf

Honeysuckle Rose

Music by Thomas "Fats" Waller
Words by Andy Razaf

E♭

Tune Up

By Miles Davis

Tune Up

By Miles Davis

B♭

Blue Haze
By Miles Davis

Moderato

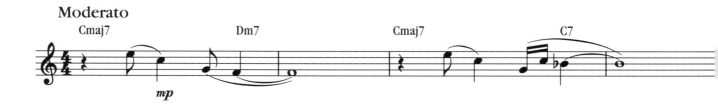

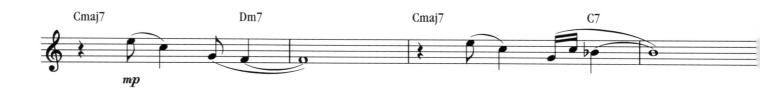

E♭

Blue Haze
By Miles Davis

Moderato

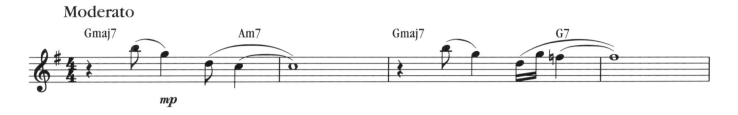

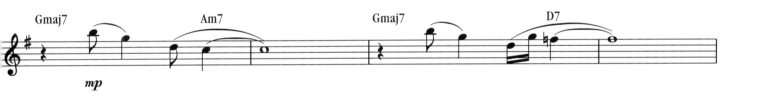

Doxy

By Sonny Rollins

B♭

Easy Groove

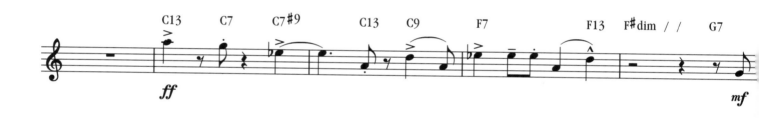

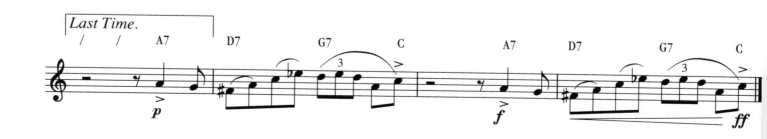

Doxy

By Sonny Rollins

E♭

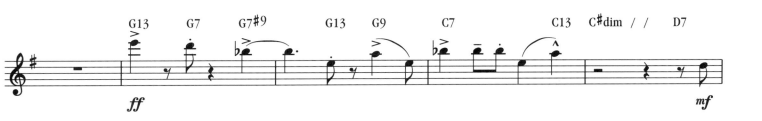

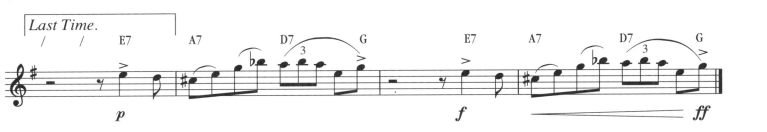

Four

By Miles Davis

B♭

Moderate Swing

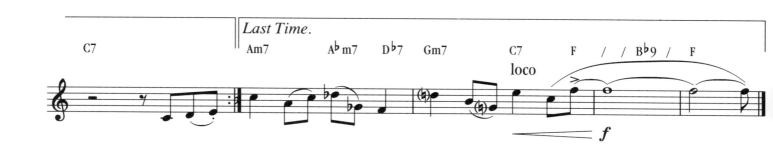

Four
By Miles Davis

Moderate Swing

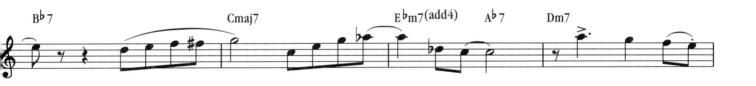

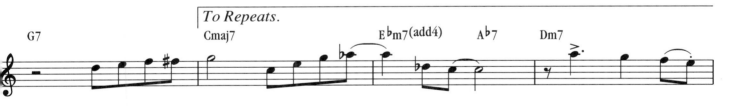

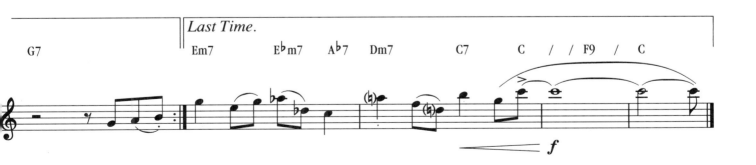

Line For Lyons

By Gerry Mulligan

B♭

Line For Lyons

By Gerry Mulligan

E♭

B♭

Why Phillis

By Eugene Wright

Moderate Jazz Waltz

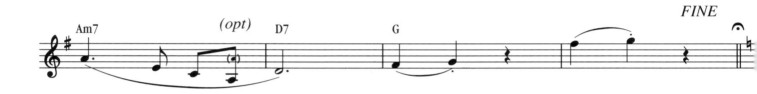

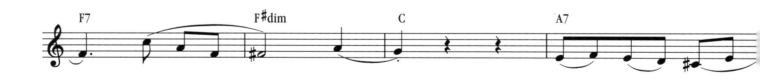

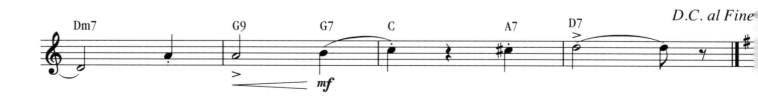

Why Phillis

By Eugene Wright

Moderate Jazz Waltz

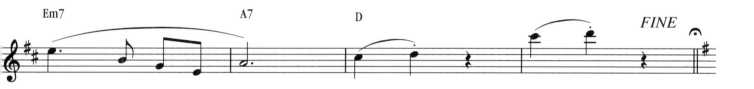

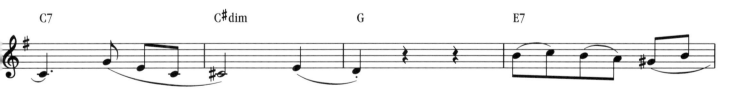

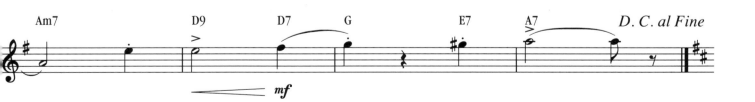

Soul Eyes

By Mal Waldron

B♭

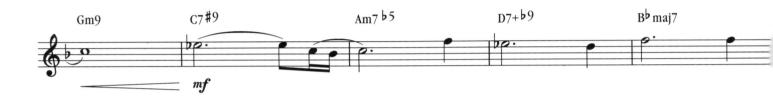

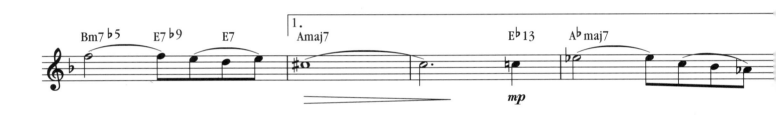

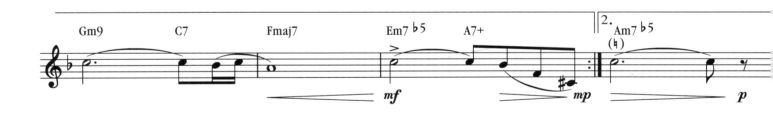

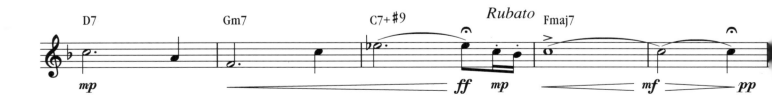

Soul Eyes

By Mal Waldron

E♭

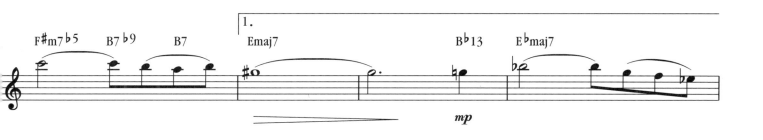

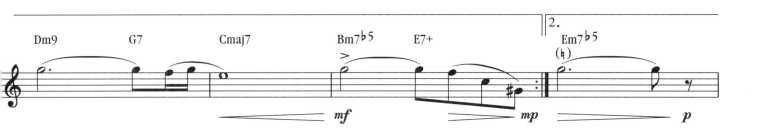

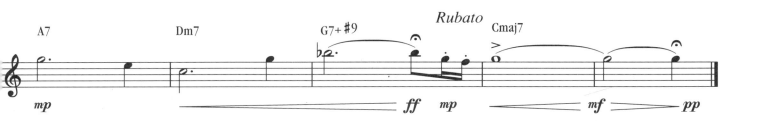

B♭

Miles Ahead
By Miles Davis

E♭

Miles Ahead
By Miles Davis

B♭

Petite Fleur (Little Flower)
Words & Music by Sidney Bechet

E♭

Petite Fleur (Little Flower)
Words & Music by Sidney Bechet

B♭

Oop Bop Sh-Bam

By John "Dizzy" Gillespie & Walter G. Fuller

Oop Bop Sh-Bam

By John "Dizzy" Gillespie & Walter G. Fuller

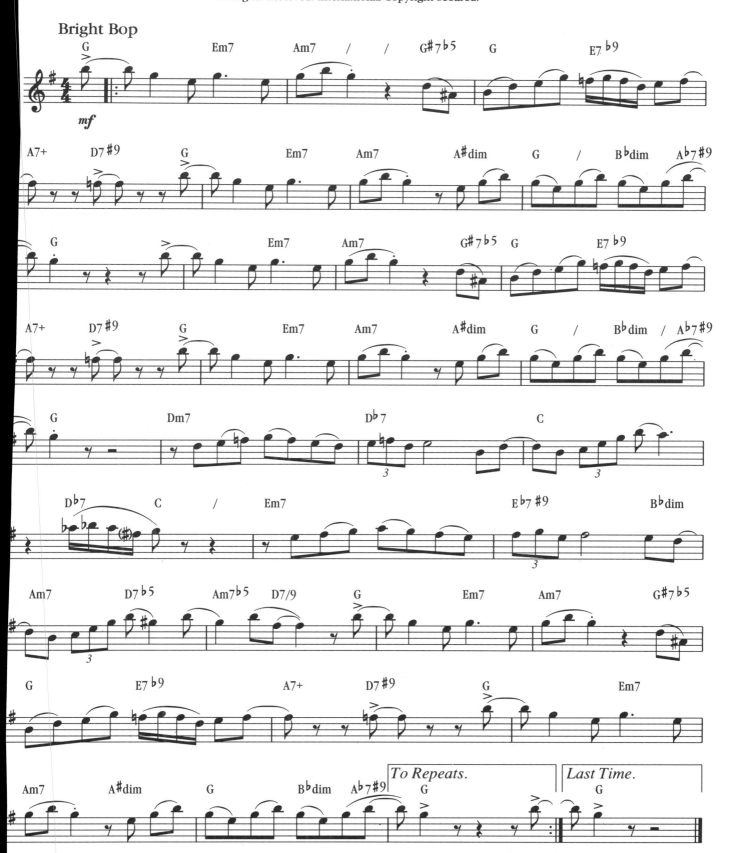

7/02(44763)

New from Music Sales - the one-and only, ultimate busker book! It's *the* book to take to a party... to a gig... on your holiday... or to that famous desert island!

It's packed with literally hundreds and hundreds of the best-loved songs of all time... from vintage standards of the 30s right through to the latest pop hits.

"The Suitcase Book"!

"Probably the best songbook in the world."

The Busker's Fake Book 1001 All-Time Hit Songs

"The only songbook you'll ever need!"

For piano, organ, guitar, all electronic keyboards and all 'C' instruments.
With an easy-to-use A-Z title finder plus a classified 'song type' index.
As a taster, here's just a quarter of the titles in this unique bumper songbook...

'A' You're Adorable
A Fine Romance
A Fool Such As I
A Hard Day's Night
A Man And A Woman
A Teenager In Love
Act Naturally
Against All Odds
Ain't Misbehavin'
All I Have To Do Is Dream
All My Loving
America
An American In Paris
An Old Fashioned Love Song
Angel Eyes
Another Suitcase In Another Hall
As Time Goes By
Band On The Run
Barbara Ann
Baubles Bangles And Beads
Because
Bennie And The Jets
Big Girls Don't Cry
Big Spender
Bird Dog
Blowin' In The Wind
Boogie Woogie Bugle Boy
Buffalo Gals
Bye Bye Love
California Dreaming
Can't Smile Without You
Candle In The Wind
Caravan
Chantilly Lace
Come Fly With Me
Consider Yourself
Crazy
Cruising Down The River
Dancing Queen
Daniel
Desafinado
Devil In Disguise
Diamonds Are A Girl's Best Friend
Do You Know The Way To San Jose
Don't Cry For Me Argentina
Don't Pay The Ferryman
Don't Sleep In The Subway
EastEnders
Ebony And Ivory
Eleanor Rigby
Empty Chairs At Empty Tables
The Entertainer
Every Breath You Take
First Time Ever I Saw Your Face
Fools Rush In
From Me To You
Funiculi, Funicula
Für Elise
Get Back
Get It On (Bang A Gong)
The Girl From Ipanema
Good Vibrations
Goodbye Yellow Brick Road
Guys And Dolls
Happy Xmas (War Is Over)
Havah Nagilah
He Ain't Heavy He's My Brother
Hello Mary Lou

Hello, Goodbye
Here, There And Everywhere
Hey Jude
Hey, Good Lookin'
Honeysuckle Rose
Came I Saw I Conga'd
I Don't Want To Spoil The Party
I Dreamed A Dream
I Feel Pretty
I Fought The Law
I Left My Heart In San Francisco
I Saw Her Standing There
I'm A Loser
I'm Beginning To See The Light
I'm Still Standing
If I Had A Hammer
If I Were A Bell
In The Air Tonight
It Never Rains In Southern California
It's Not Unusual
It's So Easy
Jambalaya
Jealous Guy
La Ronde De l'Amour
Lady D'Arbanville
The Lady In Red
The Lambeth Walk
The Last Time I Saw Paris
Layla
Leaning On A Lamp Post
Let It Be
Let's Twist Again
The Lion Sleeps Tonight
Live And Let Die
Long Tall Sally
Love And Marriage
Lover Man
Lucille
Luck Be A Lady
Lullaby Of Birdland
Maple Leaf Rag
Maria
Me And My Girl
Mister Bojangles
Money For Nothing
Mull Of Kintyre
Never On A Sunday
Nights In White Satin
Norwegian Wood
Not Fade Away
O Sole Mio
Oh Pretty Woman
Ol' Man River
Old Shep
On A Slow Boat To China
Only The Lonely
P.S. I Love You
Peggy Sue
Pennies From Heaven
Penny Lane
Pigalle
Poison Ivy
The Power Of Love
Raindrops Keep Falling On My Head
Rave On
Rhapsody In Blue
Riders On The Storm
Rock Around The Clock

Ruby Don't Take Your Love To Town
Satin Doll
Scarborough Fair
Shake Rattle And Roll
She Loves You
Singing The Blues
Sixteen Tons
Sloop John B
Smoke Gets In Your Eyes
Solitude
Something
Somewhere
Spanish Eyes
Standing On The Corner
Stars Fell On Alabama
Stranger In Paradise
Strangers In The Night
Streets Of London
Sugarbush
Sultans Of Swing
Summertime Blues
Sunshine Of Your Love
Sweet Charity
Swing Low, Sweet Chariot
Take Back Your Mink
Take That Look Off Your Face
Take The 'A' Train
Teen Angel
The Tender Trap
That'll Be The Day
Theme For A Dream
These Foolish Things
They Didn't Believe Me
This Guy's In Love With You
This Land Is Your Land
These Were The Days
Three Little Fishies
Till There Was You
To Know Him Is To Love Him
Tonight
True Love Ways
Tulips From Amsterdam
Tutti Frutti
Unchained Melody
Under The Boardwalk
Up, Up And Away
Uptown Girl
The Very Thought Of You
Wake Up Little Susie
Walk Tall
The Way You Look Tonight
We Can Work It Out
We Don't Need Another Hero
We Shall Overcome
We'll Meet Again
What Kind Of Fool Am I
Wheels
When I'm Sixty Four
When Irish Eyes Are Smiling
When This Lousy War Is Over
Where Have All The Flowers Gone
Witchcraft
With A Little Help From My Friends
Woman
Yellow Submarine
Yesterday
Your Cheatin' Heart
Your Song

Melody, lyrics and guitar chords to literally hundreds and hundreds of the best songs of all time... from the golden standards through to the great pop hits of today.

Wise Publications
Order No. AM950907

While compiling this huge book, editor/arranger Peter Lavender kept all the artwork in a huge su But now that it's printed, this new mega-bumper book is a lot easier to carry around!

Surprisingly portable, in fact, at the usual songb of 12" x 9"... with some 656 pages!

As well as the 1,001 songs, the book includes A-Z alphabetical title index *and* a classified inde